MW00791765

Lucia's Gift

by Quinn Douglas
illustrated by Pat Reynolds

SCHOOL PUBLISHERS

Copyright © by Harcourt, Inc.

All rights reserved. No part of this publication may be reproduced or transmitted in any form or by any means, electronic or mechanical, including photocopy, recording, or any information storage and retrieval system, without permission in writing from the publisher.

Requests for permission to make copies of any part of the work should be addressed to School Permissions and Copyrights, Harcourt, Inc., 6277 Sea Harbor Drive, Orlando, Florida 32887-6777. Fax: 407-345-2418.

HARCOURT and the Harcourt Logo are trademarks of Harcourt, Inc., registered in the United States of America and/or other jurisdictions.

Printed in China

ISBN 10: 0-15-350409-9
ISBN 13: 978-0-15-350409-9

Ordering Options
ISBN 10: 0-15-350332-7 (Grade 2 Below-Level Collection)
ISBN 13: 978-0-15-350332-0 (Grade 2 Below-Level Collection)
ISBN 10: 0-15-357436-4 (package of 5)
ISBN 13: 978-0-15-357436-8 (package of 5)

If you have received these materials as examination copies free of charge, Harcourt School Publishers retains title to the materials and they may not be resold. Resale of examination copies is strictly prohibited and is illegal.

Possession of this publication in print format does not entitle users to convert this publication, or any portion of it, into electronic format.

4 5 6 7 8 9 10   0940   15 14 13 12 11 10 09

Aunty Cherry is coming to visit
today. She has been on a long
trip to lots of countries. I have
really missed her!

While she was away, Aunty
Cherry sent me cards. She
bought them especially for me.

I want to give Aunty Cherry
a present when she gets
home. I think about what she
would like.

5

I take a minute to look at
the cards she sent me.
I decide to draw a picture of
each place with Aunty Cherry
in it. I'll make my pictures into
a book.

6

First, I draw Aunty Cherry in a big city.

Next, I draw her watching a
lion. Don't worry, she is safe!

8

Now Aunty Cherry is riding on a horse!

Here is Aunty Cherry riding on
an old train!

10

Finally, here she is swimming in the sea.

At the end of the book, I draw
a big picture of myself. Aunty
Cherry will be pleased to see me
in her book!

She is here! I run out to her
with my book. She gives me a
big hug.

We look at the book together.
She loves all the pictures. She
says that maybe I can go with
her on her next trip!

14

Think Critically

1. Where had Aunty Cherry been?

2. In what order did Lucia draw her pictures?

3. How do you think Lucia felt when she got a card from Aunty Cherry?

4. What did the author want you to learn from this story?

5. If you could visit another country where would you like to go? Why?

 Visual Arts

Make a Postcard Draw or paint a picture of a place you would like to visit. Then write a message to a special friend on the back of the picture.

School-Home Connection Look at the pictures Lucia drew in the book with a family member. Talk about which countries you think Aunty Cherry may have visited.